CHRISTMAS MEMORIES

Looking forward and looking back,
the best and greatest of times are shared
with those we love.

What a joy then is ours when we choose to celebrate
the miracle of heaven here on earth
with the special people in our lives.

On the pages that follow, capture those moments of celebration.
The laughter, the tender moments and even the tears you record here,
will one day help you remember much more than gifts given or miles traveled.
These words will serve as reminders...
that through the years you and yours
have given and received the greatest Christmas gift ever...
Love born in a manger and lived out in human hearts.

The purpose of the following pages is to help you as you journal your Christmas Memories. So, as the years go by, use this book to keep a record of.

- the names of special holiday guests

- the stories of the season

- favorite Christmas recipes and menus

- unusual gifts given and received

- traditions unique to your family

- tender moments spent with family